'They no longer
hold themselves
up with all their
might, but sink
a little and at that
moment appear
totally human'

ROBERT MUSIL

Born 6 November 1880, Klagenfurt, Austria-Hungary
Died 15 April 1942, Geneva, Switzerland

All pieces in this collection first published in *Nachlass zu Lebzeiten*, (*The Posthumous Papers of a Living Author*), 1936.

ALSO PUBLISHED BY PENGUIN BOOKS
The Confusions of Young Törless

ROBERT MUSIL

Flypaper

TRANSLATED BY PETER WORTSMAN

PENGUIN BOOKS

PENGUIN CLASSICS

Published by the Penguin Group
Penguin Books Ltd, 80 Strand, London WC2R ORL, England
Penguin Group (USA) Inc., 375 Hudson Street, New York, New York 10014, USA
Penguin Group (Canada), 90 Eglinton Avenue East, Suite 700, Toronto, Ontario,
Canada M4P 2Y3 (a division of Pearson Penguin Canada Inc.)
Penguin Ireland, 25 St Stephen's Green, Dublin 2, Ireland (a division of Penguin Books Ltd)
Penguin Group (Australia), 250 Camberwell Road, Camberwell, Victoria 3124, Australia
(a division of Pearson Australia Group Pty Ltd)
Penguin Books India Pvt Ltd, 11 Community Centre, Panchsheel Park,
New Delhi – 110 017, India
Penguin Group (NZ), 67 Apollo Drive, Rosedale, North Shore 0632, New Zealand
(a division of Pearson New Zealand Ltd)
Penguin Books (South Africa) (Pty) Ltd, 24 Sturdee Avenue, Rosebank, Johannesburg 2196,
South Africa

Penguin Books Ltd, Registered Offices: 80 Strand, London WC2R ORL, England

www.penguin.com

Selected from *The Posthumous Papers of a Living Author*, published by Eridanos
Press, Inc., Hygiene, Colorado 1987
Reissued by Archipelago Books, Brooklyn, New York 2006
This selection published in Penguin Classics 2011
1

Typeset by Jouve (UK), Milton Keynes
Printed in England by Clays Ltd, St Ives plc

ISBN: 978-0-141-19615-2

www.greenpenguin.co.uk

Mixed Sources
Product group from well-managed
forests and other controlled sources
www.fsc.org Cert no. SA-COC-1592
© 1996 Forest Stewardship Council

Penguin Books is committed to a sustainable future
for our business, our readers and our planet.
The book in your hands is made from paper
certified by the Forest Stewardship Council.

Contents

Flypaper

Tangle-foot flypaper is approximately fourteen inches long and eight inches wide; it is coated with a yellow poison paste and comes from Canada. When a fly lands on it – not so eagerly, more out of convention, because so many others are already there – it gets stuck at first by only the outermost joints of all its legs. A very quiet, disconcerting sensation, as though while walking in the dark we were to step on something with our naked soles, nothing more than a soft, warm, unavoidable obstruction, and yet something into which little by little the awesome human essence flows, recognized as a hand that just happens to be lying there, and with five ever more decipherable fingers, holds us tight.

Here they stand all stiffly erect, like cripples pretending to be normal, or like decrepit old soldiers (and a little bowlegged, the way you stand on a sharp edge). They hold themselves upright, gathering strength and pondering their position. After a few seconds they've come to a tactical decision and they begin to do what they can, to buzz and try to lift themselves. They continue this frantic effort until exhaustion makes them stop. Then they take a breather and try again. But the intervals grow ever longer. They stand there and I feel how helpless they are. Bewildering vapors rise from below. Their tongue gropes about like a tiny hammer. Their head is brown and hairy, as though made of a coconut, as manlike as an African idol. They twist forward and backward on their firmly fastened little legs, bend at the knees and lean forward like men trying to move a too heavy load: more tragic than the working man, truer as an athletic expression of the greatest exertion than Laocoön. And then comes the extraordinary moment when the imminent need of a second's relief wins out over the almighty instincts of self-preservation. It is the moment when the mountain climber because of the pain in his fingers willfully loosens his grip, when the man lost in the snow lays himself down like a child, when the hunted man stops dead with aching lungs. They no longer hold themselves up with all their might, but sink a little and at that moment appear totally human. Immediately they get stuck somewhere else, higher up on the leg, or behind, or at the tip of a wing.

When after a little while they've overcome the spiritual exhaustion and resume the fight for survival, they're trapped in an unfavorable position and their movements become unnatural. Then they lie down with outstretched hindlegs, propped up on their elbows and try to lift themselves. Or else seated on the ground, they rear up with outstretched arms like women who attempt in vain to wrest their hands free of a man's fists. Or they lie on their belly, with head and arms in front of them as though fallen while running, and they only still hold up their face. But the enemy is always passive and wins at just such desperate, muddled moments. A nothing, an *it* draws them in: so slowly that one can hardly follow, and usually with an abrupt acceleration at the very end, when the last inner breakdown overcomes them. Then, all of a sudden, they let themselves fall, forwards on their face, head over heels; or sideways with all legs collapsed; frequently also rolled on their side with their legs rowing to the rear. This is how they lie there. Like crashed planes with one wing reaching out into the air. Or like dead horses. Or with endless gesticulations of despair. Or like sleepers. Sometimes even the next day, one of them wakes up, gropes a while with one leg or flutters a wing. Sometimes such a movement sweeps over the lot, then all of them sink a little

deeper into death. And only on the side, near their leg-
sockets, is there some tiny wriggling organ that still
lives a long time. It opens and closes, you can't describe
it without a magnifying glass, it looks like a miniscule
human eye that ceaselessly opens and shuts.

Monkey Island

In the Villa Borghese in Rome a tall tree stands without bark or branches. It is as bald as a skull, peeled clean by sun and water, and yellow as a skeleton. It stands erect without roots and is dead, and, like a mast, is implanted in the cement of an oval island the size of a small steamboat, and separated from the kingdom of Italy by a smooth, concrete-covered ditch. This ditch is just wide enough, and on the outer side, just deep enough, so that a monkey could neither climb through it nor jump over it. From the outside in, it could probably be done, but not the other way around.

The trunk in the middle offers very good grips, and as tourists like to say, is ideal for free and easy climbing. But up on top, long, firm branches grow out horizontally; and if you were to take off your shoes and socks and with inward-hugging heels, with your soles pressed fast to the rounded branch, and your hands grasping firmly, one in front of the other, you'd have no trouble reaching the end of one of these long, sun-soaked branches that stretch out over the green, ostrich-feathered peaks of the pines.

This wonderful island is settled by three families of varying size and number. About fifteen sinewy, nimble boys and girls, all about the size of a four-year-old child, inhabit the tree; while at the foot of the tree, in the only building on the island, a palace, the shape and size of a doghouse, a couple of far mightier monkeys live with a very small son. This is the island's royal couple and the crown prince. Never do the old ones wander far from home; like watchmen, motionless, they sit to the right and left of him and stare down their snouts into the distance. Only once every hour the king rouses himself and mounts the tree for a perambulating look around. Slowly he then steps along the boughs, and it doesn't seem that he cares to notice how reverentially and distrustfully everyone shrinks back, and – to avoid a stir – they slink over sideways till the end of the branch permits no further retreat, and nothing but a perilous leap down to the hard concrete is left. So the king strides the length of the boughs, one after the other, and the most acute attentiveness cannot decipher whether all the while his face evinces the discharge of a ruler's duty or a survey of the grounds. Meanwhile, on the palace roof the crown prince sits alone, for astonishingly his mother also always departs at the same time, and through his thin, wide, stick-out ears the sun shines coral-red. Seldom can one see a thing so dumb and pathetic, and yet so much encompassed by an invisible dignity, as this young monkey. One after the other, the tree monkeys, who were chased to the ground, file past him, and could easily twist off his skinny neck with a single grip: they're in an awful mood, but they make a wide detour around him and display all the reverence and reserve that his family is due.

It takes a long time to notice that aside from these beings who live such a well-ordered life, still others inhabit the island. Driven from the surface and the air, a large population of little monkeys live in the ditch. If one of them even shows his face on the island above, he is chased by the tree monkeys back into the ditch, under severe reprisals. At feeding time the little ones must sit timidly to the side, and only when the others are full and mostly at rest up in the tree, are they permitted to sneak over to the crumbs. They're not even allowed to touch what's thrown to them. A nasty boy or a tricky girl are often just waiting for the chance. Though with a wink they may feign indigestion, they carefully slip down from their perch, as soon as they notice that the little ones are having too good a time. Those few who dared climb up onto the island are already scurrying screaming back into the ditch; and they mingle with the others; and the howling outcry begins: And now they all press together, so that a single surface of hair and flesh and mad, dark eyes swell up against the outer wall like water in a tipped-over tub. The persecutor, however, only walks along the edge and shoves the wave of shuddering terror back away from himself. Thereupon the little black faces stir and they throw up their arms and stretch out their palms in supplication before the evil foreign eye that gazes down from the edge. And soon this gaze attaches itself to one individual; he shoves backwards and forwards, and five others do it with him, who can't yet make out which one of them is the target of this long look; but the weak, fear-crippled mass of monkeys does not budge. Then the long, indifferent gaze nails its arbitrary victim; and at last it's completely impossible to control oneself any longer, not to show either too much or too little fear: and from one moment to the next the lapse of self-control swells, while one soul digs into another, till the hate is there, and the crack gives way, and without shame or poise a creature whines under torture. With the release of a scream, the others rush apart on down the ditch; they flicker dimly about like the damned souls in the flames of purgatory, and gather chattering cheerfully as far from the scene as possible.

When it's all over with, the persecutor climbs with a feathery grip up the big tree to its highest branch, strides out to the very end of the branch, peacefully seats himself, and serious, erect, and ever so long, he stays like that without rousing. The beam of his glance glides over the Pincio and the Villa Borghese; and where it leaves the gardens behind, there beneath it lies the great yellow city, over which, still swathed in the green shimmering cloud of the tree top, it floats, oblivious to all, suspended in midair.

Fishermen on the Baltic

On the beach they've dug out a little pit with their hands, and from a sack of black earth they're pouring in fat earthworms; the loose black earth and the mass of worms make for an obscure, moldy, enticing ugliness in the clean white sand. Beside this they place a very tidy looking wooden chest. It looks like a long, not particularly wide drawer or counting board, and is full of clean yarn; and on the other side of the pit another such, but empty, drawer is placed.

The hundred hooks attached to the yarn in the one drawer are neatly arranged on the end of a small iron pole and are now being unfastened one after the other and laid in the empty drawer, the bottom of which is filled with nothing but clean wet sand. A very tidy operation. In the meantime, however, four long, lean and strong hands oversee the process as carefully as nurses to make sure that each hook gets a worm.

The men who do this crouch two by two on knees

and heels, with mighty, bony backs, long, kindly faces, and pipes in their mouths. They exchange incomprehensible words that flow forth as softly as the motion of their hands. One of them takes up a fat earthworm with two fingers, tears it into three pieces with the same two fingers of the other hand, as easily and exactly as a shoemaker snips off the paper band after he's taken the measurement; the other one then presses these squirming pieces calmly and carefully onto each hook. This having been accomplished, the worms are then doused with water and laid in neat, little beds, one next to the other, in the drawer with the soft sand, where they can die without immediately losing their freshness.

It is a quiet, delicate activity, whereby the coarse fishermen's fingers step softly as on tiptoes. You have to pay close attention. In fair weather the dark blue sky arches above, and the seagulls circle high over the land like white swallows.

Sheep, As Seen in Another Light

As to the history of sheep: Today man views the sheep as stupid. But God loved it. He repeatedly compared man with sheep. Is it possible that God was completely wrong?

As to the psychology of sheep: The finely chiseled expression of exalted consciousness is not unlike the look of stupidity.

On the heath near Rome: They had the long faces and the delicate skulls of martyrs. Their black stockings and hoods against the white fur reminded of morbid monks and fanatics.

When they rummaged through the low, sparse grass, their lips trembled nervously and scattered the timbre of a quivering steel string over the earth. Joined in chorus, their voices rang out like the lamentations of prelates in the cathedral. But when many of them sang together, they formed a men's, women's, and children's choir. In soft swells they lifted and lowered their voices; it was like a wandering train in the darkness, struck every other second by light, and the children's voices then stood on an ever-returning hill, while the men strode through the valley. Day and night rolled a thousand times faster through their song and drove the earth onwards to its end. Sometimes a solitary voice flung itself up or tumbled down in fear of damnation. Heaven's clouds were recreated in the white ringlets of their hair. These are age-old catholic animals, religious companions of mankind.

Once again in the South: Man is twice as big as usual in their midst and reaches like a church spire up toward heaven. Beneath our feet the earth was brown, and the grass like scratched-in grey-green stripes. The sun shone heavy on the sea as on a lead mirror. Boats were busy fishing as in Saint Peter's time. The cape swung the view like a running board up toward heaven and broke off into the dark yellow and white sea as in wandering Odysseus' day.

Everywhere: When man approaches, sheep are timid and stupid; they have known the beatings and stones of his insolence. But if he stands stock still and stares into the distance, they forget about him. They stick their heads together then, ten or fifteen of them, and form the spokes of a wheel, with the big, heavy center-point of heads and the otherwise-colored spokes of their backs. They press their skulls tightly together. This is how they stand, and the wheel that they form won't budge for hours. They don't seem to want to feel anything but the wind and the sun, and between their foreheads, the seconds striking out eternity that beats in their blood and signals from head to head like the hammering of prisoners on prison walls.

Sarcophagus Cover

Somewhere to the rear of the Pincio, or already in Villa Borghese, two sarcophagus covers of a common sort of stone lie out in the open between the bushes. They constitute no rare treasure, they're just lying around. Stretched out on top of them, the couple who once as a final memento had themselves copied in stone, are at rest. One sees many such sarcophagus covers in Rome; but in no museum and in no church do they make such an impression as here under the trees, where as though on a picnic, the figures stretched themselves out, and seem just to have awakened from a little sleep that lasted two thousand years.

They've propped themselves up on their elbows and are eyeing each other. All that's missing between them is the basket of cheese, fruit, and wine.

The woman wears a hairdo of little curls – any minute now she'll arrange them according to the latest fashion from the time before she fell asleep. And they're smiling at each other; a long, a very long smile. You look away: and still they go on smiling.

This faithful, proper, middle-class, beloved look has lasted centuries; it was sent forth in ancient Rome and crosses your glance today.

Don't be surprised that even in front of you it endures, that they don't look away or lower their eyes: this doesn't make them stone-like, but rather all the more human.

Monuments

Aside from the fact that you never know whether to refer to them as monuments or memorials, monuments do have all kinds of other characteristics. The most salient of these is a bit contradictory; namely, that monuments are so conspicuously inconspicuous. There is nothing in this world as invisible as a monument. They are no doubt erected to be seen – indeed, to attract attention. But at the same time they are impregnated with something that repels attention, causing the glance to roll right off, like water droplets off an oilcloth, without even pausing for a moment. You can walk down the same street for months, know every address, every show window, every policeman along the way, and you won't even miss a dime that someone dropped on the sidewalk; but you are very surprised when one day, staring up at a pretty chambermaid on the first floor of a building, you notice a not-at-all-tiny metal plaque on which, engraved in indelible letters, you read that from eighteen hundred and such and such to eighteen hundred and a little more the unforgettable So-and-so lived and created here.

Many people have this same experience even with larger-than-life-sized statues. Every day you have to walk around them, or use their pedestal as a haven of rest, you employ them as a compass or a distance marker; when you happen upon the well-known square, you sense them as you would a tree, as part of the street scenery, and you would be momentarily stunned were they to be missing one morning but you never look at them, and do not generally have the slightest notion of whom they are supposed to represent, except that maybe you know if it's a man or a woman.

It would be wrong to let ourselves be deceived by certain exceptions to the rule. As, for instance, those few statues which, Baedeker in hand, we seek out, like the Gattamelata or the Colleoni, this being a very particular example; or memorial towers that block off an entire landscape; or monuments that form a series, like the Bismarck monuments scattered all over Germany.

Such forceful monuments do exist; and then there are also those that embody the expression of a living thought or feeling: it is, however, the purpose of most ordinary monuments to first conjure up a remembrance, or to grab hold of our attention and give a pious bent to our feelings, for this, it is assumed, is what we more or less need; and it is in this, their prime purpose, that monuments always fall short. They repel the very thing they are supposed to attract. One cannot say we did not notice them; one would have to say they 'de-notice' us, they elude our perceptive faculties: this is a downright vandalism-inciting quality of theirs!

This can no doubt be explained. Anything that endures over time sacrifices its ability to make an impression. Anything that constitutes the walls of our life, the backdrop of our consciousness, so to speak, forfeits its capacity to play a role in that consciousness. A constant, bothersome sound becomes inaudible after several hours. Pictures that we hang up on the wall are in a matter of days soaked up by the wall; only very rarely do we stand before them and look at them. Half-read books once replaced among the splendid rows of books in our library will never be read to the end. Indeed, it is enough for some sensitive souls to buy a book whose beginning they like, and then never pick it up again. In this case, the attitude is already becoming outright aggressive; one can, however, also follow its inexorable course in the realm of feelings, in which case it is always aggressive, in family life, for instance. Here the firm bond of marriage is distinguished from the fickleness of desire by the much-repeated sentence: Do I have to tell you every fifteen minutes that I love you?! And to what heightened degree must these psychological detriments of durability manifest themselves in bronze and marble!

If we mean well by monuments, we must inevitably come to the conclusion that they make demands on us that run contrary to our nature, and for the fulfillment of which very particular preparations are required. It would be a crime to want to make the danger signs for cars as inconspicuously monochrome as monuments. Locomotives, after all, blow shrill, not sleepy tones, and even mailboxes are accorded alluring colors. In short, monuments ought also to try a little harder, as we must all do nowadays! It is easy for them to stand around quietly, accepting occasional glances; we have a right to ask more of our monuments today. Once we have grasped this idea – which, thanks to certain current conceptual tendencies, is slowly making inroads – we recognize how backward our monument art is in comparison to contemporary developments in advertising. Why doesn't our bronze-cast hero at least resort to the gimmick, long since outdated elsewhere, of tapping with his finger on a pane of glass? Why don't the figures in a marble group turn, like those better-made figures in show windows do, or at least blink their eyes open and shut? The very minimum that we ought to ask of monuments, to make them attract attention, would be tried and true logos, like 'Goethe's *Faust* is the best!' or 'The dramatic ideas of the famous poet X are the cheapest!'

Unfortunately, the sculptors won't have any of this. They do not, so it seems, comprehend our age of noise and movement. If they represent a man in civilian clothes, he sits motionlessly in a chair or stands there, his hand stuck in between the second and third button of his jacket. Sometimes he also holds a scroll in his hand, and no expression flutters across his face. He generally looks like one of the acute melancholics in the mental hospitals. If people were not oblivious to monuments and could observe what was going on up there, they'd shudder when passing, as you do beside the walls of a madhouse. It is even more frightening when the sculptors depict a general or a prince. His flag is waving in his hand, and there's no wind. His sword is drawn and no one draws back in fear. His arm motions imperiously forwards, and no man would think of following him. Even his horse, rearing, with splayed nostrils, ready to jump, remains balanced on its hindlegs, astonished that the people down below, instead of stepping aside, quietly stuff a sandwich into their mouths or buy a paper. By God, the figures in monuments never make a move and yet remain forever frozen in a faux pas. It is a desperate situation.

I believe that I have in these remarks contributed a little something to the understanding of monument figures, memorial plaques, and the like. Maybe someone or other will henceforth look at them on his way home. But what I find ever more incomprehensible, the more I think about it, is the question, Why then, matters being the way they are, are monuments erected precisely for great men? This seems to be a carefully calculated insult. Since we can do them no more harm in life, we thrust them with a memorial stone hung around their neck into the sea of oblivion.

The Paintspreader

If over the course of the years you are compelled to pass through painting exhibitions, then surely one day you are bound to invent the term paintspreader. He is to the painter what the penpusher is to the poet. The term gives order to a hodgepodge of disparate phenomena. Since the beginning of our reckoning of time penpushers have lived off adaptations of the ten commandments and a few fables handed down to them by antiquity; the assumption that paintspreading is likewise based on a few fundamental principles is not therefore altogether out of the question.

Ten such principles would not be too few. For if you apply ten artistic principles effectively, that is, combined in alternating order, the result, mistakes in calculation notwithstanding, is three million, six-hundred twenty-eight thousand, and eight hundred different combinations. Each of these combinations would be different from the others, and all of them nonetheless still the same. The connoisseur could spend his life counting: one-two-three-four-five . . ., two-one-three-four-five . . ., three-two-one-four-five . . . and so on. Naturally the connoisseur would be indignant and would perceive this as a threat to his accomplished abilities.

It also seems that after several hundred thousand paint-spreaders the whole business would become ridiculous, and they would then switch artistic 'directions.' You can see what an artistic direction is, the moment you set foot in an exhibition hall. You would be more hard-pressed to recognize it, if you had to pass before a single solitary painting; but spread over many walls, artistic schools, directions, and periods are as easily distinguishable, one from another, as wallpaper patterns. On the other hand, the theoretical underpinnings of these various schools, directions, and periods usually remain unclear. This is by no means meant as a slight upon the paintspreaders; they produce honest work, are well-versed in their craft and are personally, for the most part, distinctive fellows. But the production statistics level out all differences.

We do however have to acknowledge one disadvantage that works against them: the fact that their paintings hang openly on the wall. Books have the advantage of being bound, and often uncut. They therefore stay famous longer; they maintain their freshness, and fame, after all, begins at that point at which you have heard of something but are not familiar with it. The paintspreaders, on the other hand, have the advantage of being more regularly sought out and 'written up' than are the penpushers. If it weren't for the art market, how difficult it would be to decide which work you prefer! Christ, in his day, drove the dealers out of the Temple: I, however, am convinced that if you possess the true faith, you must also be able to sell it; then you could also adorn yourself with it, and then there would be a great deal more faith in the world than there is now!

Another advantage enjoyed by painting is that there is a method to it. Anyone can write. Perhaps everyone can paint too, but this fact is less well-known. Techniques and styles were invented to envelop painting in a shroud of mystery. Not everyone can paint like someone else; to do that, you have to first learn how. Those elementary-school children so rightfully admired nowadays for their painting talents would flunk out in any art academy; but the academic painter must likewise take great pains to unlearn his acquired technique in order to drop his conventions and draw like a child. It is, all in all, a historic error to believe that the master makes the school; the students make it!

If we examine the matter more closely, however, it is not true either that anyone can write; quite the contrary, nobody can – everyone can merely take dictation and copy. It is impossible that a poem of Goethe's could come into being today; and even if, by some miracle, Goethe were to write it himself, it would still be an anachronistic and in many ways dubious new poem, even though a splendid masterpiece of old! Is there any other explanation for this mystery than that this poem would not seem as though it had been copied from any contemporary poem, except perhaps for those poems that were themselves copied from it? Contemporaneity always means copying. Our ancestors wrote prose in long, beautiful sentences, convoluted like curls; although we still learn to do it that way in school, we write in short sentences that cut more quickly to the heart of the matter; and no one in the world can free his thinking from the manner in which his time wears the cloak of language. Thus no man can know to what extent he actually means what he writes and in writing, it is far less that people twist words than it is that words twist people.

Is it possible then too that not everyone can paint after all? Clearly, the painter cannot, not in the sense that the paintspreader associates with the word. The painter and the poet are above all, in the eyes of their contemporaries, those who cannot do what the paintspreaders and the penpushers can do. This is why so many penpushers consider themselves poets and so many paintspreaders painters. The difference usually only becomes apparent once it's too late. For by that time, a new generation of pushers and spreaders have come of age who already know what the painter and poet have only just learned.

This also explains why the painter and the poet always appear to belong to the past or the future; they are forever being awaited or declared extinct. If, however, on occasion one actually happens to pass for the real thing, it isn't always necessarily the right one.

It's Lovely Here

There are many people who on their vacations are drawn to famous places. They drink beer in their hotel gardens, and if in addition they happen to make pleasant acquaintances, they already look forward to the memories. On the last day of their vacation they go to the nearest stationers; they buy picture postcards there, and then buy more postcards from the waiter back at the hotel. The picture postcards that these people buy look the same all over the world. They are tinted: the trees and lawns, poison green; the sky, peacock blue; the cliffs are grey and red. The houses are presented in downright painful relief, as though at any moment they might spring up out of the surface; and the color is so intense that a narrow band of it generally forms a contour on the flip side of the card. If the world really looked like that, one could indeed do nothing better than affix a stamp to it and toss it in the nearest mailbox. On these picture postcards people write: 'It is indescribably beautiful here.' Or 'It's lovely here.' Or: 'Too bad you couldn't be here with me to see all this beauty.' Sometimes they also write: 'You have no idea how beautiful it is here.' Or: 'What a swell time we're having here!'

You really do have to understand these people correctly! They are very happy indeed to be on a vacation trip and to see so many beautiful things that others cannot see; but it causes them pain and embarrassment actually to have to look at these things. If a tower is taller than other towers, a precipice deeper than the common precipice or a famous painting particularly large or small, that is all right, for the difference can be ascertained and talked about; it is for this reason that they tend to seek out a famous palace that is particularly spacious or particularly old, and among landscapes they prefer the wild ones. If you could only trick them about train schedules, hotel rates, and uniforms (but that is just what they would never fall for!), and set them down unawares on a cliff in the Saxon Switzerland, you could no doubt convince them to feel a genuine Matterhorn thrill, for surely Saxony is dizzying enough. If, however, something is not high, deep, large, small, or strikingly painted, in short, if something is not a phenomenon worth talking about, but merely beautiful, they choke – as though on a big smooth bite that will neither go up nor down, a morsel too soft to suffocate on, and too tough to let a word pass. Thus emerge those Oohs! and Ahs!, painful syllables of suffocation. You cannot very well reach with your fingers down your throat; and we have not yet found a better means of getting the necessary words out of our mouth. It isn't right to make fun of this. Such exclamations express a very painful feeling of constriction.

Experienced art commentators naturally have their own special techniques about which we might well have something to say; but this would be going too far. And, moreover, even the uncorrupted average man, despite the disagreeable effects of his constriction, feels a genuine satisfaction when standing face to face, as it were, with something that is acknowledged by experts as beautiful. This satisfaction has its own curious nuances. It contains for instance some of the same pride you feel when you can say that you passed the bank building at the very same hour when the famous bank robber X must have made his escape; other people already feel enraptured just to set foot in the city in which Goethe spent eight days, or to know the cousin by marriage of the lady who first swam the English Channel; there are indeed people who find it particularly wonderful just to live in such a momentous era. It always seems to revolve around a having-been-there; though in general it requires some element of complication, it must have an air of personal exclusivity. For as much as people lie, pretending to be completely engrossed in their occupations, they take a childish delight in personal experiences and that incalculable sense of importance that such experiences give us. It is then that they feel touched by their own 'personal destiny,' which is an altogether extraordinary thing: 'He was just talking to me at that very moment when he slipped and broke his leg . . .!' What they feel, were they to be able to put it into words, is as if, behind that great blue window with the cloud curtains, someone had been standing a long time watching them.

And you may not want to believe it, but it is usually for this very reason alone that we ourselves travel to those places depicted in the postcards we buy, a tendency which does not in and of itself make sense, since it would after all be much easier simply to order the cards by mail. And this is the reason why such postcards have to be so overbearingly and over-realistically beautiful; if ever they were to start looking natural, then mankind would have lost something. 'So this is what it looks like here,' we say to ourselves and study the card mistrustfully; then we write below: 'You can't imagine how lovely it is . . .!'' It is the same manner of speaking by which one man confides in another: 'You can't imagine how much she loves me . . .'

The Blackbird

The two men whom I must mention in order to relate three little stories, in which the narrative pivots around the identity of the narrator, were friends from youth; let's call them Aone and Atwo. The fact is that such early friendships grow ever more astounding the older you get. You change over the years, from the crown of your head to the soles of your feet, from the skin's soft down to the depths of your heart, but strangely enough, your relationship with each other stays the same, fluctuating about as little as the communion we each carry on with that diverse host of sirs successively addressed as *I*. It is beside the point whether or not you still identify with that little blond numskull photographed once long ago; as a matter of fact, you can't really say for sure that you even like the little devil, that bundle of I. And so too, you may very well both disagree with and disapprove of your best friends; indeed, there are many friends who can't stand each other. And in a certain sense, those friendships are the deepest and the best, for without any admixtures, they contain that indefinable essence in its purest form.

The youth that united the two friends Aone and Atwo was nothing less than religious in character. While both were brought up in an institution that prided itself on the proper emphasis it placed on the religious fundamentals, the pupils of that institution did their best to ignore those selfsame principles. The school chapel, for instance, was a real, big, beautiful church, complete with a stone steeple; it was reserved for the school's exclusive use. The absence of strangers proved a great boon, for while the bulk of the student body was busy according to the dictates of sacred custom, now kneeling, now rising at the pews up front, small groups could gather at the rear to play cards beside the confessional booths, or to smoke on the organ steps. And some escaped up the steeple, whose pointed spire was ringed by a saucer-like balcony on the stone parapet of which, at a dizzying height, acrobatics were performed that could easily have cost the lives of far less sin-burdened boys than these.

One such provocation of the Lord involved a slow, muscle-straining elevation of the feet in midair, while with glance directed downwards, you grasped the parapet, balancing precariously on your hands. Anyone who has ever tried this stunt on level ground will appreciate just how much confidence, bravery, and luck are required to pull it off on a foot-wide stone strip up at the top of a tower. It must also be said that many wild and nimble boys, though virtuoso gymnasts on level ground, never did attempt it. Aone, for instance, never tried it. Atwo, on the other hand – and let this serve to introduce him as narrator – was, in his boyhood, the creator of this test of character. It was hard to find another body like his. He didn't sport an athletic build like so many others, but seems to have developed muscles naturally, effort-lessly. A narrow smallish head sat atop his torso, with eyes like lightning bolts wrapped in velvet, and teeth that one would sooner have associated with the fierce-ness of a beast of prey than the serenity of a mystic.

Later, during their student days, the two friends pro-fessed a materialist philosophy of life devoid of God or the soul, viewing man as a physiologic or economic machine – which in fact he may very well be, though this wasn't the point as far as they were concerned: since the appeal of such a philosophy lies, not in its inherent truth, but rather in its demonic, pessimistic, morbidly intellectual character. By this time their relationship had already become that special kind of friendship. And while Atwo studied forestry, and spoke of traveling as a forest ranger to the far reaches of Russia or Asia, as soon as he was through with his studies, his friend Aone,

who scorned such boyish aspirations, had by then settled on a more solid pursuit, and had at the time already
cast in his lot with the rising labor movement. And
when they met again shortly before the Great War. Atwo
already had his Russian adventure behind him. He spoke
little about it, was now employed in the offices of some
large corporation, and seemed, despite the appearance
of middle-class comfort, to have suffered considerable
disappointments. His old friend had in the meantime
left the class struggle and become editor of a newspaper
that printed a great deal about social harmony and was
owned by a stock broker. Henceforth the two friends
despised each other insuperably, but once again fell out
of touch; and when they finally met again for a short
while, Atwo told the following story the way one emp-
ties out a sack of memories for a friend, so as to be able
to push on again with a clean bill of lading. It matters
little under the circumstances how the other responded,
and their exchange can perhaps best be related in the
form of a monologue. It would be far more important
to the fabric of the tale were it possible to describe
exactly what Atwo looked like at the time (which is easier said than done), for this raw impression of the man is
not without bearing on the gist of his words. Suffice it to
say that he brought to mind a sharp, taut, and narrow
riding crop balanced on its soft tip, leaning up against

the wall; it was in just such a half-erect, half-slouching posture that he seemed to feel most at ease.

Among the most extraordinary places in the world – said Atwo – are those Berlin courtyards where two, three, or four buildings flash their rear ends at each other, and where, in square holes set in the middle of the walls, kitchen maids sit and sing. You can tell by the look of the red copper pots hung in the pantry how loud their clatter is. From far down below a man's voice bawls curses up at one of the girls, or heavy wooden shoes go clip clop back and forth across the cobblestones. Slowly. Heavily. Incessantly. Senselessly. Forever. Isn't it so?

The kitchens and bedrooms look outwards and downwards on all this; they lie close together like love and digestion in the human anatomy. Floor upon floor, the conjugal beds are stacked up one on top of the other; since all the bedrooms occupy the same space in each building – window wall, bathroom wall, and closet wall prescribe the placement of each bed almost down to the half yard. The dining-rooms are likewise piled up floor on floor, as are the white-tiled baths and the balconies with their red awnings. Love, sleep, birth, digestion, unexpected reunions, troubled and restful nights are all vertically aligned in these buildings like the columns of sandwiches at an automat. In middle-class apartments like these your destiny is already waiting for you the moment you move in. You will admit that human freedom consists essentially of where and when we do what we do, for what we do is almost always the same: thus the sinister implications of one uniform blueprint for all. Once I climbed up on top of a cabinet just to make use of the vertical dimension, and I can assure you that the unpleasant conversation in which I was involved looked altogether different from that vantage point.

Atwo laughed at the memory and poured himself a drink; Aone thought about how they were at that very moment seated on a balcony with a red awning that belonged to his apartment, but he said nothing, knowing all too well what he might have remarked.

I am still perfectly willing to admit today, by the way – Atwo added of his own accord – that there is something awe-inspiring about such uniformity. And in the past this sense of vastness, of a wasteland, brought to mind a desert or an ocean; a Chicago slaughterhouse (as much as the image may turn my stomach) is after all quite different from a flower pot! But the curious thing was that during the time I occupied that apartment, I kept thinking of my parents. You recall that I had almost lost contact with them – but then all of a sudden this thought came to me out of nowhere: they gave you your life. And this ridiculous thought kept coming back again and again like a fly that refuses to be shooed away. There's nothing more to be said about this sanctimonious notion ingrained in us in early childhood. But whenever I looked over my apartment, I would say to myself: there, now you've bought your life, for so and so many marks a month rent. And sometimes maybe I also said: now you've built up a life for yourself with your own two hands. My apartment served as some odd amalgamation of a warehouse, a life-insurance policy and a source of pride. And it seemed so utterly strange, such an inscrutable mystery that there was something which had been given to me whether I wanted it or not; and, moreover, that that something functioned as the very foundation of everything else. And I believe that that banal thought concealed a wealth of abnormality and unpredictability, all of which I had kept safely hidden from myself. And now comes the story of the nightingale.

It began on one evening much like any other. I'd stayed home, and after my wife had gone to bed, I sat myself down in the study; the only difference that night was that I didn't reach for a book or anything else, but this too had happened before. After one o'clock the street starts getting quieter; conversations become a rarity; it is pleasant to follow the advent of evening with your ear. At two o'clock all the clamor and laughter below have clearly tipped over into intoxication and lateness. I realized that I was waiting for something, but I didn't know what for. By three o'clock – it was May – the sky grew lighter; I felt my way through the dark apartment to the bedroom and lay down without a sound. I expected nothing more now but sleep, and that the next morning would bring a day like the one that had just passed. And soon I no longer knew whether I was awake or asleep.

In the space between the curtains and the blind a dark greenness gushed forth; thin bands of the white froth of morning seeped in between the slats. This might have been my last waking impression or a suspended dream vision. Then I was awakened by something drawing near; sounds were coming closer. Once, twice I sensed it in my sleep. Then they sat perched on the roof of the building next door and leaped into the air like dolphins. I could just as well have said, like balls of fire at a fireworks display, for the impression of fireballs lingered; in falling, they exploded softly against the windowpanes and sank to the earth like great silver stars. Then I experienced a magical state; I lay in my bed like a statue on a sarcophagus cover, and I was awake, but not like during the day. It is very difficult to describe, but when I think back, it is as though something had turned me inside out; I was no longer a solid, but rather a something sunken in upon itself. And the air was not empty, but of a consistency unknown to the daylight senses, a blackness I could see through, a blackness I could feel through, and of which I too was made. Time pulsed in quick little fever spasms. Why should something not happen now that normally never happens? – It's a nightingale singing outside! – I said half aloud to myself.

Well, maybe there are more nightingales in Berlin than I thought – Atwo continued. At the time I believed that there were none in this stony preserve, and that this one must have flown to me from far away. To me! – I felt it and sat up with a smile. A bird of paradise! So it does indeed exist! – At such a moment, you see, it seems perfectly natural to believe in the supernatural; it is as if you'd spent your childhood in an enchanted kingdom. And I immediately decided: I'll follow the nightingale. Farewell, my beloved! – I thought – farewell, my beloved, my house, my city. . . ! But before I had even gotten up out of bed, and before I had figured out whether to climb up to the nightingale on the rooftop, or to follow it on the street down below, the bird had gone silent and apparently flown away.

Now he's singing from some other rooftop for the ears of another sleeper, Atwo mused. – You're probably thinking that this was the end of the story? – But it was only the beginning, and I have no idea what end it will take!

I'd been abandoned, left behind with a heavy heart. That was no nightingale, it was a blackbird, I said to myself – just as you'd like to say to me right now. Everyone knows that such blackbirds imitate other birds. By this time I was wide awake and the silence bored me. I lit a candle and considered the woman who lay next to me. Her body had the color of pale bricks. The white border of the blanket lay over her skin like a lip of snow. Wide shadow lines of mysterious derivation ringed her body – mysterious even though they must of course have had something to do with the candle and the position of my arms. So what, I thought, so what if it really was only a blackbird! The very fact that an ordinary blackbird could have had such a crazy effect on me: that makes the whole thing all the more extraordinary! For as you well know: while a single disappointment may elicit tears, a repeated disappointment will evoke a smile. And meanwhile I kept looking at my wife. This was all somehow connected, but I didn't know how. For years I've loved you – I thought to myself – like nothing else in this world, and now you lie there like a burnt-out husk of love. You're a stranger to me now, and I've arrived at the other end of love. Had I grown tired of her? I can't remember ever having felt sated. Let me put it like this, it was as if a feeling could drill its way through the heart as though through a mountain, and find another world on the other side, a world with the same valley, the same houses and the same little bridge. In all honesty, I simply had no idea what was happening. And I still don't understand it today. Perhaps it's wrong of me to tell you this story in connection with two others that happened afterwards. I can only tell you how I saw it during the experience: as a signal from afar – so it seemed to me at the time.

I lay my head beside her body that slept on unawares, and took no part in all this. Then her bosom seemed to rise and fall more strenuously than before, and the walls of the room lapped up against this sleeping form like waves against a ship far out at sea. I would probably never have been able to bring myself to say goodbye; but if I were to slip away right now, I told myself, then I'd stay the little lost boat, past which a great sturdy ship would sail unnoticing. I kissed her sleeping form, she didn't feel it. I whispered something in her ear, and maybe I did it so quietly that she wouldn't hear it. Then I ridiculed myself and sneered at the very thought of the nightingale; but quietly nonetheless I got dressed. I think that I cried, but I really did leave. I felt giddy, light-hearted, even though I tried to tell myself that no decent human being would do such a thing; I remember that

I was like a drunkard rebuking the sidewalk beneath his feet to reassure himself that he's sober.

Of course, I often thought of returning; at times I would have liked to cross half the world to get back to her, but I never did. She had become untouchable to me; in short – I don't know if you understand – he who has committed an injustice and feels it down to the bone, can no longer set it aright. I am not, by the way, asking for absolution. I just want to tell you my stories to find out if they ring true. For years I haven't been able to tell them to anyone, and had I heard myself talking to myself, I would quite frankly have questioned my sanity.

Please be assured then that my reason is still the equal of your enlightened mind.

Then, two years later, I found myself in a tight fix, at the dead angle of a battle line in the south Tyrol, a line that wound its way from the bloody trenches of the Cima di Vezzena all the way to Lake Caldonazzo. There, like a wave of sunshine, the battle line dived deep into the valley, skirting two hills with beautiful names, and surfaced again on the other side, only to lose itself in the stillness of the mountains. It was October; the thinly manned trenches were covered with leaves, the lake shimmered a silent blue, the hills lay there like huge withered wreaths; like funeral wreaths, I often thought to myself without even a shudder of fear. Halting and divided, the valley spilled around them; but beyond the edge of our occupied zone, it fled such sweet diffusion and drove like the blast of a trombone: brown, broad, and heroic out into the hostile distance.

At night we pushed ahead to an advanced position, so prone now in the valley that they could have wiped us out with an avalanche of stones from above; but instead, they slowly roasted us with steady artillery fire. The morning after such a night all our faces had a strange expression that took hours to wear off: our eyes were enlarged, and our heads tilted every which way on the multitude of shoulders, like a lawn that had just been trampled on. Yet on every one of those nights I poked my head up over the edge of the trench many times, and cautiously turned to look back over my shoulder like a lover: and I saw the Brenta Mountains light blue, as if formed out of stiff-pleated glass, silhouetted against the night sky. And on such nights the stars were like silver-foil cut-outs, glimmering, fat as glazed cookies; and the sky stayed blue all night; and the thin virginal moon crescent lay on her back, now silvery, now golden, basking in the splendor. You must try to imagine just how beautiful it was: for such beauty exists only in the face of danger. And then sometimes I could stand it no longer,

47

and giddy with joy and longing, I crept out for a little nightcrawl around, all the way to the golden-green blackness of the trees, so enchantingly colorful and black, the like of which you've never seen.

But things were different during the day; the atmosphere was so easygoing that you could have gone horseback riding around the main camp. It's only when you have the time to sit back and think and to feel terror that you first learn the true meaning of danger. Every day claims its victims, a regular weekly average of so and so many out of a hundred, and already the divisional general staff officers are predicting the results as impersonally as an insurance company. You do it too, by the way. Instinctively you know the odds and feel insured, although not exactly under the best of terms. It is a function of the curious calm that you feel, living under constant crossfire. Let me add the following though, so that you don't paint a false picture of my circumstances. It does indeed happen that you suddenly feel driven to search for a particular familiar face, one that you remember seeing several days ago; but it's not there anymore. A face like that can upset you more than it should, and hang for a long time in the air like a candle's afterglow. And so your fear of death has diminished, though you are far more susceptible to all sorts of strange upsets. It is as if the fear of one's demise, which evidently lies on top of man forever like a stone, were suddenly to have been rolled back, and in the uncertain proximity of death an unaccountable inner freedom blossoms forth.

Once during that time an enemy plane appeared in the sky over our quiet encampment. This did not happen often, for the mountains with their narrow gaps between fortified peaks could only be hazarded at high altitudes. We stood at that very moment on the summit of one of those funereal hills, and all of a sudden a machine-gun barrage spotted the sky with little white clouds of shrapnel, like a nimble powder puff. It was a cheerful sight, almost endearing. And to top it off, the sun shone through the tricolored wings of the plane as it flew high overhead, as though through a stained-glass church window, or through colored crepe paper. The only missing ingredient was some music by Mozart. I couldn't help thinking, by the way, that we stood around like a crowd of spectators at the races, placing our bets. And one of us even said: better take cover! But nobody it seems was in the mood to dive like a field mouse into a hole. At that instant I heard a distant ringing drawing closer to my ecstatically upturned face. Of course, it could also have happened the other way around, that I first heard the ringing and only then became conscious of the impending danger; but I knew immediately: it's an aerial dart. These were pointed iron rods no thicker than a pencil lead that planes dropped from above in those days. And if they struck you in the skull, they came out through the soles of your feet, but they didn't hit very often, and so were soon discarded. And though this was my first aerial dart – bombs and machine-gun fire sound altogether different – I knew right away what it was. I was excited, and a second later I already felt that strange, unlikely intuition: it's going to hit!

And do you know what it was like? Not like a frightening foreboding, but rather like an unexpected stroke of good luck! I was surprised at first that I should be the only one to hear its ringing. Then I thought the sound would disappear again. But it didn't disappear. It came ever closer, and though still far away, it grew proportionally louder. Cautiously I looked at the other faces, but no one else was aware of its approach. And at that moment when I became convinced that I alone heard that subtle singing, something rose up out of me to meet it: a ray of life, equally infinite to that death ray descending from above. I'm not making this up, I'm trying to put it as plainly as I can. I believe I've held to a sober physical description so far, though I know of course that to a certain extent it's like in a dream where it seems as though you're speaking clearly, while the words come out all garbled.

It lasted a long time, during which I alone heard the sound coming closer. It was a shrill, singing, solitary, high-pitched tone, like the ringing rim of a glass; but there was something unreal about it. You've never heard anything like it before, I said to myself. And this tone was directed at me; I stood in communion with it and had not the least little doubt that something decisive was about to happen to me. I had no thoughts of the kind that are supposed to come at death's door, but all my thoughts were rather focused on the future; I can only say that I was certain that in the next second I would feel God's proximity close up to my body – which, after all, is saying quite a bit for someone who hasn't believed in God since the age of eight.

Meanwhile, the sound from above became ever more tangible; it swelled and loomed dangerously close. I asked myself several times whether I should warn the others; but let it strike me or another, I wouldn't say a word! Maybe there was a devilish vanity in this illusion that high above the battlefield a voice sang just for me. Maybe God is nothing more than the vain illusion of us poor beggars who puff ourselves up in the pinch and brag of rich relations up above. I don't know. But the fact remains that the sky soon started ringing for the others too; I noticed traces of uneasiness flash across their faces, and I tell you – not one of them let a word slip either! I looked again at those faces: fellows, for whom nothing would have been more unlikely than to think such thoughts, stood there, without knowing it, like a group of disciples waiting for a message from on high. And suddenly the singing became an earthly sound, ten, a hundred feet above us and it died. He – it – was here. Right here in our midst, but closer to me, something that had gone silent and been swallowed up by the earth, had exploded into an unreal hush.

My heart beat quickly and quietly; I couldn't have lost consciousness for even a second; not the least fraction of a second was missing from my life. But then I noticed everyone staring at me. I hadn't budged an inch but my body had been violently thrust to the side, having executed a deep, one hundred-and-eighty degree bow. I felt as though I were just waking from a trance, and had no idea how long I'd been unconscious. No one spoke to me at first; then, finally, someone said: 'An aerial dart!' And everyone tried to find it, but it was buried deep in the ground. At that instant a hot rush of gratitude swept through me, and I believe that my whole body turned red. And if at that very moment someone had said that God had entered my body, I wouldn't have laughed. But I wouldn't have believed it either – not even that a splinter of His being was in me. And yet whenever I think back to that incident, I feel an overwhelming desire to experience something like it again even more vividly!

I did by the way experience it one more time, but not more vividly – Atwo began his last story. He seemed to grow suddenly unsure of himself, but you could see that for that very reason he was dying to hear himself tell the story.

It had to do with his mother, for whom Atwo felt no great love, though he claimed it wasn't so. – On a superficial level, we just weren't suited to each other, he said, and that, after all, is only natural for an old woman who for decades has lived in the same small town, and a son who according to her way of thinking never amounted to much. She made me as uneasy as one would be in the presence of a mirror that imperceptibly distorts the width of one's image; and I hurt her by not coming home for years. But every month she wrote me an anxious letter, asking many questions, and even though I hardly ever wrote back, there was still something extraordinary about it; and despite all, I felt a strong tie to her, as the following incidents would soon prove.

Decades ago, perhaps, the image of a little boy had inscribed itself indelibly in her imagination – a boy in whom she may have set God knows what aspirations – this image could not thereafter be erased by any means; and since that long-gone little boy happened to be me, her love clung to me, as though all the suns that have set since then were gathered somewhere, suspended between darkness and light. Here it is again: that strange vanity that is not vain. For I can assure you that I don't like to dwell on myself, nor as so many others do, to smugly stare at photographs of the person they once were, or delight in memories of what they did in such and such a place at such and such a time; this sort of savings bank account of self is absolutely incomprehensible to me. I am neither particularly sentimental, nor do I live for the moment; but when something is over and done with, then I am also over and done with that something in myself. And when on some street I happen to remember having often walked that way before, or when I see the house I used to live in, then even without thinking, I feel something like a shooting pain, an intense revulsion for myself, as though I had just been reminded of a terrible disgrace. The past drifts away as you change; and it seems to me that in whatever way you change, you wouldn't do so if that fellow you left behind had been all that flawless. But for the very reason that I usually feel this way, it was wonderful to realize that there was a person who had for my entire life preserved this image of me, an image which most likely never bore me any likeness, which nonetheless was in a certain sense the mandate of my being and my deed to life.

Can you understand me when I say that my mother was in this figurative capacity a veritable lioness, though in her real life she was locked in the persona of a manifestly limited woman? She was not bright, by our way of thinking; she could disregard nothing and came to no major conclusions about life; nor was she, when I think back to my childhood, what you'd call a good person: she was vehement and always on edge. And you can well imagine what comes from the combination of a passionate nature and limited horizons – but I would like to suggest that another kind of stature, another kind of character still exists side by side with the embodiment that human beings take on in their day-to-day existence, just as in fairy-tale times the Gods took on the forms of snakes and fish.

Not long after that incident with the aerial dart, I was taken prisoner during a battle in Russia. I consequently experienced a big change, and wasn't so quick about getting back home, since this new life appealed to me for quite a while. I still admire the socialist system, but then one day I found that I could no longer mouth a few of the essential credos without a yawn, and so I eluded the perilous repercussions by escaping back to Germany, where individualism was just reaching its inflationary peak. I got involved in all sorts of dubious business ventures, in part out of necessity, in part simply for the pleasure of being back in a good old-fashioned country, where you can misbehave and not have to feel ashamed of yourself. Things weren't going all that well for me then, and at times I'd say things were downright rotten. My parents weren't doing so well either. And then my mother wrote me several times: we can't help you, son; but if the little you'll one day inherit would be of any help, then I'd wish myself dead for your sake. This she wrote to me even though I hadn't visited her in years, nor had I shown the least little sign of affection. I have to admit though that I took this for a somewhat exaggerated manner of speaking, and paid it no mind, though I didn't doubt the honesty of feeling couched in these sentimental words. But then an altogether extraordinary thing happened: my mother really did fall ill, and it appears as if she then took along my father, who was very devoted to her.

Atwo reflected – She died of an illness that she must have been carrying around in her without anyone knowing it. One might suppose that it was the confluence of numerous natural causes, and I fear that you'll think badly of me if I don't accept this explanation. But here again, the incidental circumstances proved remarkable. She definitely didn't want to die; I know for a fact that she fought it off and railed against an early death. Her will to live, her convictions, and her hopes were all set against it. Nor can it be said that a resolve of character overruled her inclinations of the moment; for if that were so, she could have thought of suicide or voluntary poverty long ago, which she by no means did. She was her own total sacrifice. But have you never noticed that your body has a will of its own? I am convinced that the sum total of what we take to be our will, our feelings and thoughts – all that seems to control us – is allowed to do so only in a limited capacity; and that during serious illness and convalescence, in critical combat, and at all turning points of fate, there is a kind of primal resolve of the entire body that holds the final sway and speaks the ultimate truth.

But be that as it may; I assure you that my mother's illness immediately gave me the impression of something self-willed. Call it my imagination, but the fact still remains that the moment I heard the news of my mother's illness, a striking and complete change came over me, even though the message suggested no imminent cause for alarm. A hardness that had encompassed me melted away instantaneously; and I can say no more than that the state I now found myself in bore a great resemblance to my awakening on that night when I left my house, and to the moment of my anticipation of the singing arrow from above. I wanted to visit my mother right away, but she held me off with all sorts of excuses. At first she sent word that she looked forward to seeing me, but that I should wait out the lapse of this insignificant illness, so that she could welcome me home in good health. Later she let it be known that my visit would upset her too much for the moment. And finally, when I insisted, I was informed that recovery was imminent and that I should just be patient a little while longer. It seems as though she feared that a reunion between us might cause her to waiver in her resolve. And then everything happened so quickly, that I just barely still made it to the funeral.

I found my father likewise ailing when I got there, and as I told you, all I could do then was to help him die. He'd been a kind man in the past, but in those last weeks he was astonishingly stubborn and moody, as though he held a great deal against me and resented my presence. After his funeral I had to clear out the household, which took another few weeks; I was in no particular hurry. Now and then neighbors came by out of old force of habit, and told me just exactly where in the living room my father used to sit, where my mother would sit, and where they themselves would. They looked everything over carefully and offered to buy this or that. They're so thorough, those small-town types; and once after thoroughly inspecting everything, one of them said to me: It's such a shame to see an entire family wiped out in a matter of weeks! – I of course didn't count. When I was alone, I sat quietly and read children's books; I found a big box full of them up in the attic. They were dusty, sooty, partly dried out and brittle, partly sodden from the dampness, and when you struck them they gave off an unending stream of soft black clouds; the streaked paper had worn off the cardboard bindings, leaving only jagged archipelagos of paper behind. But as soon as I turned the pages, I swept through their contents like a sailor piloting his way across the perilous high sea, and once I made an extraordinary discovery. I noticed that the blackness at the top corner where you turned the pages and at the bottom edge of each book differed in a subtle but unmistakable way from the mildew's design, and then I found all sorts of indefinable spots, and finally, wild faded pencil markings on the title pages. And suddenly it came to me, and I realized that this impetuous disrepair, these pencil scrawls and hastily made spots were the traces of a child's fingers, my own child fingers, preserved for thirty-some odd years in a box in the attic, and long forgotten!

Well, as I told you, though it may for some people not be an earth-shattering event to remember themselves, it was for me as if my life had been turned upside down. I also discovered a room that thirty and some odd years ago had been my nursery; later it was used to store linen and the like, but the room had essentially been left the way it was when I sat there at my pine-wood table beneath the kerosene lamp whose chain was decorated with three dolphins. There I sat once again for many hours a day, and read like a child whose legs are too short to touch the floor. For you see, we are accustomed to an unbounded head, reaching out into the empty ether, because we have solid ground beneath our feet. But childhood means to be as yet ungrounded at both ends, to still have soft flannel hands, instead of adult pincers, to sit before a book as though perched on a little leaf soaring over bottomless abysses through the room. And at that table, I tell you, I really couldn't reach the floor.

I also set myself a bed in this room and slept there. And then the blackbird came again. Once after midnight I was awakened by a wonderful, beautiful singing. I didn't wake up right away, but listened first for a long time in my sleep. It was the song of the nightingale; she wasn't perched in the garden bushes, but sat instead on the rooftop of a neighbor's house. Then I slept on a while with my eyes open. And I thought to myself: there are no nightingales here, it's a blackbird.

But don't think this is the same story I already told you today! No – because just as I was thinking: there are no nightingales here, it's a blackbird – at that very moment, I woke up. It was four in the morning, daylight streamed into my eyes, sleep sank away as quickly as the last trace of a wave is soaked up by the dry sand at the beach. And there, veiled in daylight as in a soft woolen scarf, a blackbird sat in the open window! It sat there just as sure as I sit here now.

I am your blackbird – it said – don't you remember me?

I really didn't remember right away, but I felt happy all over while the bird spoke to me.

I sat on this window sill once before, don't you remember? – it continued, and then I answered: yes, one day you sat there just where you now sit, and I quickly closed the window, shutting it in.

I am your mother – it said.

This part, I admit, I may very well have dreamed. But the bird itself I didn't dream up; she sat there, flew into my room, and I quickly shut the window. I went up to the attic and looked for a large wooden bird cage that I seemed to remember, for the blackbird had visited me once before – in my childhood, like I just told you. She sat on my window sill and then flew into my room, and I needed a cage. But she soon grew tame, and I didn't keep her locked up anymore, she lived free in my room and flew in and out. And one day she didn't come back again, and now she had returned. I had no desire to worry about whether it was the same blackbird; I found the cage and a new box of books to boot, and all I can tell you is that I had never before been such a good person as from that day on: the day I had my blackbird back again – but how can I explain to you what I mean by being a good person?

Did she often speak again? – Aone asked craftily.

No – said Atwo – she didn't speak. But I had to find birdfood for her and worms. You can imagine that it was rather difficult for me: I mean the fact that she ate worms, and I was supposed to think of her as my mother – but it's possible to get used to anything, I tell you, it's just a matter of time – and don't most everyday matters likewise take getting used to! Since then I've never let her leave me, and that's about all I have to tell; this is the third story, and I don't know how it's going to end.

But aren't you implying – Aone cautiously inquired – that all this is supposed to have a common thread?

For God's sake, no – Atwo countered – this is just the way it happened; and if I knew the point of it all, then I wouldn't need to have told it in the first place. But it's like hearing a whisper and a rustling outside, without being able to distinguish between the two!

a little history

Penguin Modern Classics were launched in 1961, and have been shaping the reading habits of generations ever since.

The list began with distinctive grey spines and evocative pictorial covers – a look that, after various incarnations, continues to influence their current design – and with books that are still considered landmark classics today.

Penguin Modern Classics have caused scandal and political change, inspired great films and broken down barriers, whether social, sexual or the boundaries of language itself. They remain the most provocative, groundbreaking, exciting and revolutionary works of the last 100 years (or so).

In 2011, on the fiftieth anniversary of the Modern Classics, we're publishing fifty Mini Modern Classics: the very best short fiction by writers ranging from Beckett to Conrad, Nabokov to Saki, Updike to Wodehouse. Though they don't take long to read, they'll stay with you long after you turn the final page.

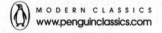